Dead Man's Bend

The Dead Man Files

by

Alan Combes

Illustrated by Stephen Elford

First published in 2009 in Great Britain by
Barrington Stoke Ltd
18 Walker St, Edinburgh, EH3 7LP

www.barringtonstoke.co.uk

Title ISBN: 978-1-84299-650-8
Pack ISBN: 978-1-84299-725-3

Printed in Great Britain by the Charlesworth Group

TOP SECRET

Dead Man File

Name: Luke Smith

Age: 16

Cause of death: Car crash. Serious head and back injuries.

Date of case 1: May 2009

Mission: To pay back the guy who killed me.

DMF

To Chris Garford and Ernie Mason

Contents

Chapter 1

My best pal, Joe, is alive and well, but I am dead. I'm Luke. I will tell you how I died and why Joe lives on.

It was all Joe's idea.

He nicked the car.

He got the booze. He asked the girls along.

Name:
Luke Smith
Age:
16

Chapter 2

Joe was the driver when the car smashed into the wall. I yelled at him from the passenger seat.

"Look out, man, there's a patch of ice."
(The last thing I saw.)

The girls screamed. (The last thing I heard.)

Name:
Luke Smith
Age:
16

Chapter 3

The two girls and Joe finished up in hospital.

Me? I was so smashed up my mum could not even tell the dead body was me.

Joe got away with it. The police said it was just one of those things. They knew he had nicked the car. They never knew about speeding and how much booze the driver had.

Now I (Luke), want my revenge.

Name:
Luke Smith
Age:
16

Chapter 4

Now I am a ghost. I hide in Joe's car. When he walks up to his car he sees me in it and he freezes.

He looks again and I am gone. Were his
eyes fooling him?

When he goes to bed at night, I whisper in his ear, "I'm watching you, Joe."

He sits up in terror, but can't see me anywhere.

Name:
Luke Smith
Age:
16

Chapter 5

Joe meets again the two girls who were in the crash. He is so cool. He wants to impress them.

My ghostly face smiles at the girls above his head. The girls can see me but Joe can't.

The girls scream and run away. No one wants Joe for a friend.

Name:
Luke Smith
Age:
16

Chapter 6

Then I do my best trick. I wait until he
is driving along the same road where I died.

At the bend, he sees my ghost in his head-lights.

Joe is so afraid that he loses control of the car.

It skids across the road smashing at 70 miles an hour into the same wall that took my life.

Silence. Joe has just joined me in the world of ghosts.

Like this book? Why not try the next one?

Saving Stan

Luke Smith is dead. But he's back to help those who need it.

A tramp in the woods is in danger.

Can Luke save him?

For more info check out our website:
www.barringtonstoke.co.uk

Watch out for more Dead Man Files books ...

Spiker

Yasmin's drink is spiked. Can Luke warn her in time?

Fire Escape

Dan is in danger. Can Luke help him?

For more info check out our website:
www.barringtonstoke.co.uk